Contents

First published 2014 by Brown Watson
The Old Mill, 76 Fleckney Road
Kibworth Beauchamp
Leicestershire LE8 0HG

ISBN: 978 0 7097 2181 9

© 2014 Brown Watson, England

Reprinted 2015

Printed in Malaysia

Now I Can
READ
Animal Stories

Written by Lisa Regan

Illustrated by Gill Guile

Brown Watson
ENGLAND

Mouse on the Moon

Kieran is a little mouse with a big imagination. Last night, as he gazed up at the shining disc in the sky, he wondered what it would be like to go to the Moon.

'It looks like a big, round cheese with a bite taken out of it!' he thought, as he drifted off to sleep on the sofa.
His little whiskers twitched as he dreamed.

Kieran dreams that he is on a mission to explore the Moon. The countdown begins and the rocket begins to shake. Kieran grips the controls tightly as the rocket blasts off.

'I will be the first mouse on the Moon!' he squeaks, and sets his course through the emptiness of space. He checks his equipment and waits excitedly to see the Moon. There it is! Kieran expertly guides the rocket down to land gently on the surface.

Kieran examines the Moon's surface. It is soft and crumbly. He bends down and twitches his whiskery nose. The Moon smells of cheese! He lifts a rock in his paw and nervously takes a bite.
It IS cheese!

Suddenly, Kieran sees lots of strange creatures running towards him, waving their arms. As he picks up more cheesy rocks, the creatures growl. They don't want him to steal the moon cheese. 'Time to go home!' he squeaks, and blasts off to safety!

Read these words again

strange   emptiness

dreams   whiskers

creatures   equipment

mission   expertly

rocket   nervously

surface   countdown

shining   imagination

Did you see these things?

The Moon

Rocket

Cheese on toast

Aliens

Planet

Naughty Monkey

The jungle animals are having great fun. They are playing a game called Blind Man's Buff. They take turns to wear a blindfold and then chase after their friends. When they catch someone they must guess who it is.

It is Lion's turn but he is having trouble guessing. 'Your skin feels like Elephant's, but where is your trunk?' he growls.

What has happened to the animals? Elephant's trunk has become a tiny little snout. Giraffe's legs and neck are much shorter than normal. And no one can catch Tortoise because all of a sudden he can run very fast.

They are very puzzled. Then they hear laughing coming from the tree above. 'Hee hee, it's me!' chuckles Monkey. 'I cast a spell on you all!'

Naughty Monkey has stolen Fairy Flora's spell book, and she is extremely cross. She takes it back and tells him off. Then she waves her wand to undo the spell that Monkey has made.

Fairy Flora waves her wand a second time, and mutters under her breath. Now it is Monkey's turn to be puzzled. She has turned him into a banana until he learns his lesson!

Read these words again

playing	guessing
banana	giraffe
snout	blindfold
trunk	puzzled
shorter	naughty
laughing	chuckles
trouble	extremely

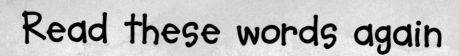

Did you see these things?

Wand

Blindfold

Spell book

Cross fairy

Tortoise

Best Behaviour

Kerry is a little koala who finds it easy to get into trouble. Today, she dropped her school bag and made it all dirty. Yesterday, she left her lunchbox at school, so she had nothing to keep her lunch in today.

Her mummy tries not to get cross, but it is hard when Kerry does something wrong every day. 'Please try to be good,' begs her mummy, and gives Kerry a hug.

Kerry's best friend is a kangaroo called Gina. She does her best to look out for Kerry, and to keep her out of trouble. She calls for Kerry every morning and they walk to school together.

Today is a sunny day and they are both feeling happy. Kerry has written down everything she needs to remember to keep out of trouble. She tucks her notepad into the pocket on her tummy to keep it safe.

In class, Kerry sits quietly. She puts her hand up, and waits to be asked to speak. At lunchtime, she throws away her rubbish. She packs her lunchbox into her bag to take home. Then she puts her bag on its hook, to keep it safe.

After school, Gina asks why Kerry is smiling. Kerry shows her list, with a big tick next to everything she remembered. 'Well done!' says Gina. 'Let's go and show your mum!'

Read these words again

friend	something
school	remember
written	everything
trouble	yesterday
speak	today
rubbish	morning
dirty	quietly

Did you see these things?

Lunchbox

Butterfly

Bag

Notebook

Snail

Ladybird

Happy to Help

Mrs Badger is one of the oldest animals in the woods. She often needs help with her shopping. Today she has run out of bread.

'We'll go and get it for you!' squeak Tim and Tom the mice. They love to be helpful. Mrs Badger thanks them, and gives them a drink and a snack for their journey.

Tim and Tom scamper off along the track. After a while, they sit down to eat their snack. A little rabbit hops past looking sad. 'Hello!' shout the helpful mice. 'What's wrong?'

The rabbit explains that she has been travelling for ages and is very thirsty. Tim offers her their bottle of drink. In a flash, the rabbit throws off her furry disguise and reveals herself as a fairy. 'You are so kind!' she says, and conjures up a lovely picnic as a reward.

The little mice are very excited. They hurry back to the woods, pushing their special picnic in front of them. Their friends all come out to see what the mice are squeaking about.

'We got a magic picnic as a reward from a fairy!' they explain. Tim and Tom unpack the food and share it with all of the animals. There is cake and fruit – and even bread for old Mrs Badger.

Read these words again

share	helpful
magic	oldest
special	scamper
friends	picnic
thirsty	conjures
excited	journey
reward	disguise

Did you see these things?

Apple

Fairy

Cake

Hedgehog

Glasses

Butterfly

Tearful Toby

Sally Songbird is worried. She has seen Toby the warthog looking very sad indeed. She calls out to her other flying forest friends, and they all flutter around Toby to find out what's wrong.

'I have no proper friends,' he says sadly. 'I think the other animals are frightened of my tusks, and don't want to play.' He curls up next to a tree and a big teardrop trickles down his bristly cheek.

'Surely that's not true,' says Sally Songbird. 'The forest is full of friendly creatures. Won't Katy Fox or Susie Squirrel play with you?' Toby sighs. He explains that Susie and Katy are always whispering about him.

Sally decides to find out what's going on, and flies off to speak to Katy Fox. Within five minutes, she is back, and she seems very excited. 'Follow me!' she chirps to Toby.

Toby gallops through the trees
and into a clearing, where he
comes to a sudden stop.
There is another warthog
staring back at him!

'Toby, meet Tabitha!' chirrups
Sally Songbird. The other
animals thought that Toby
looked sad and lonely, and
wondered how they could help.
They searched the whole forest,
and had seen Tabitha playing
by herself. That's what they had
been whispering about!

Read these words again

tusks	friendly
proper	worried
flying	explains
lonely	teardrop
animals	bristly
whisper	trickles
excited	frightened

Did you see these things?

Tusks

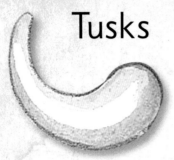

Bushy tail

Butterfly

Ladybird

Pink
snout

Mice

Songbird

Shark Attack!

Life on a coral reef is great fun. The fish swim around happily together, and the coral makes a fantastic playground for their games.

Pia the pipefish shoots out of a hole to make Plato the pufferfish jump. When he is startled he swells up like a balloon, and Pia thinks it is hilarious!

Lucy the lobster and Salim the squid swim over to join in the fun. They are deciding what to play next, when a huge, dark shadow passes over them in the sea above.

'Shark! Hide!' they all cry, and dive for cover in the nooks and crannies of the coral reef. The enormous shark swims closer and closer until they can see his beady eyes.

Surprisingly, the shark doesn't attack them, but cries out in pain and twists from side to side. Pia can see that he has a sharp piece of coral stuck between his teeth. Bravely, she swims out from her hiding place and offers to help.

The shark feels better as soon as Pia removes the coral from his mouth. Now he wants to join in their games as well — and he is very good at playing 'It'!

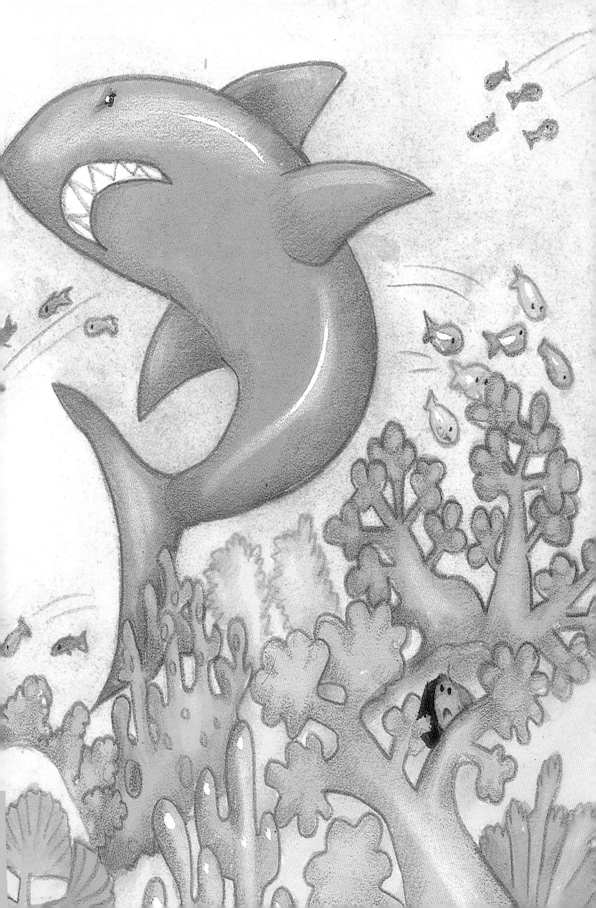

Read these words again

games	balloon
attack	playground
hiding	fantastic
enormous	startled
shadow	happily
deciding	surprisingly
lobster	hilarious

Did you see these things?

Coral

Shell

Lobster

Pipefish

Limpet

School
of fish

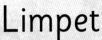

Team Spirit

It is the day of the trials for Bunny United, and Archie Rabbit is very excited. He loves playing football and is hoping that he will be picked for the team.

Archie puts on his football kit and packs his boots in his bag. Then he races along to the football pitch to meet the others. He does feel very nervous!

Archie tries his hardest, but
there are a lot of players who
are better than him. The coach
picks his team, and Archie is not
chosen. He packs up his boots
and walks away sadly.

Archie looks up when he hears
a mewing noise from a tree.
Two mean crows are picking on
a little kitten! Archie picks up
some mud to throw at the crows
and scare them away.

The crows fly off, cawing noisily, but the little kitten can't get down. 'Jump!' says Archie. 'I'll catch you!' The kitten leaps from the tree and safely into Archie's arms.

'Good catch!' says a voice behind him. 'And good throwing, too! Would you like to join my cricket team?' Archie smiles proudly. He is going to be a member of a sports team after all!

Read these words again

pitch	mewing
throw	nervous
catch	trials
players	noisily
proudly	hardest
chosen	playing
voice	picked

Did you see these things?

Football

Kit bag

Crow

Cricket bat

Kitten

Happy Birthday

Sheldon is a very, very old tortoise. He has lived a long and happy life on a tropical island, basking in the sunshine and slowly chewing leaves. He plods around, munching and thinking, and then munching some more.

Soon it will be Sheldon's birthday, and he decides to have a party. He writes invitations to all of his family and friends. How exciting!

Lots and lots of tortoises come to Sheldon's party to help him celebrate. They sing and dance and play party games. Their game of musical statues lasts for days!

Sheldon is very happy indeed to see all of his young relatives. They crowd around him to hear his stories about the olden days, when he was just a little tortoise.

One tiny tortoise crawls up to
Sheldon to ask him something.
'How old actually ARE you?'
he enquires.

'That's a very good question,'
laughs Sheldon. 'Do you know,
when I sent out the invitations
I was going to be celebrating
my 99th birthday. But it took
so long for all of my guests
to arrive, that now I am 100!
Happy birthday to me!'

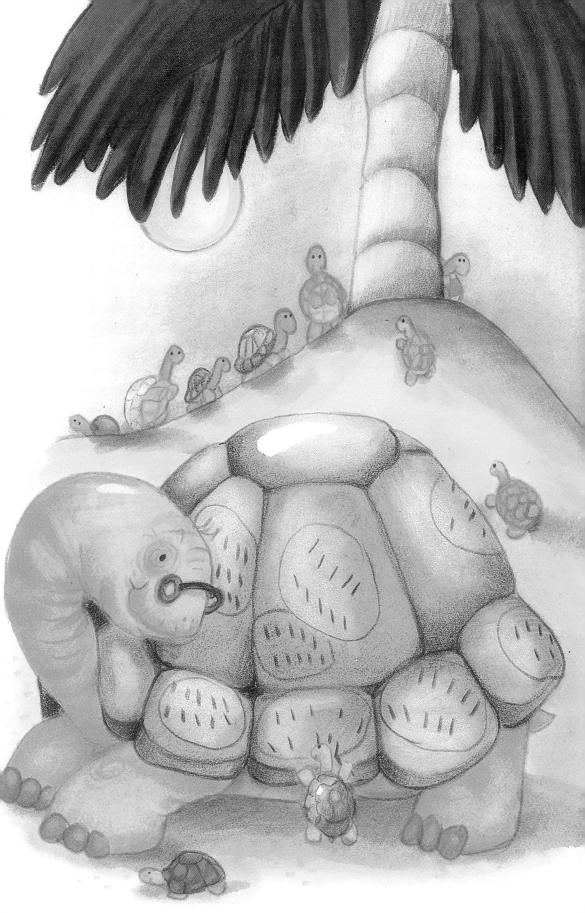

Read these words again

plods	tropical
slowly	basking
stories	relatives
sunshine	munching
olden days	thinking
celebrate	chewing
musical	decides

Did you see these things?

Invitation

Balloon

Party
hat

Pen

Present

Tortoise

Go Slow

There is a feeling of excitement in the jungle today. Lion has organised a race, and lots of the animals want to take part. Lion is feeling very confident that his team will win.

He explains the rules to everyone. They must form teams of three, and tie their legs so they have to work together to run without falling over. Lion fastens his leg to his friend Zebra, who is also tied to Crocodile.

When Elephant trumpets, the teams start running. Lion's team zooms off and soon leaves the others behind. But they are going so fast they don't see a fallen tree, and they fall over in a tangled heap.

'Come on!' trumpets Elephant. He, Rhino and Giraffe are surely big and strong enough to win the race now. However, Giraffe is so tall that his neck becomes tangled in the jungle vines, and they have to stop.

The smallest team in the race is also the slowest. Turtle and Tortoise can't run fast at all, and Sloth is even slower! But they plod along carefully, overtaking the others who are still caught up in a mess.

The team crosses the finish line in first place. They are the winners! They hold the trophy in the air proudly and get a cheer from everyone. Sometimes slow and steady is just what you need!

Read these words again

vines	trumpets
finish	explains
feeling	organised
winners	confident
steady	together
trophy	fastens
tangled	however

Did you see these things?

Trophy

Finish line

Bee

Team Tiny

Snail

Flower

Hide and Squeak

'Who wants to play hide and seek?' squeaks Suki Shrew. She is in the mood for a fun game with her friends. Ginger cat agrees to be the seeker, and closes her eyes while the others run off to hide.

Suki dives behind a tree and waits until Ginger shouts, 'Coming, ready or not...' With a twitch of her nose, Ginger smells where Suki Shrew is hiding, and pads off silently to find her.

As Ginger gets closer to Suki, she begins to purr. Suki hears her, and creeps away from her hiding place to run back to the safety of the counting post.

Suki is trying so hard not to be seen that she doesn't notice a hole in the ground. She tumbles down it and rolls deep into the earth. 'Miaow!' says Ginger. 'That's cheating!'

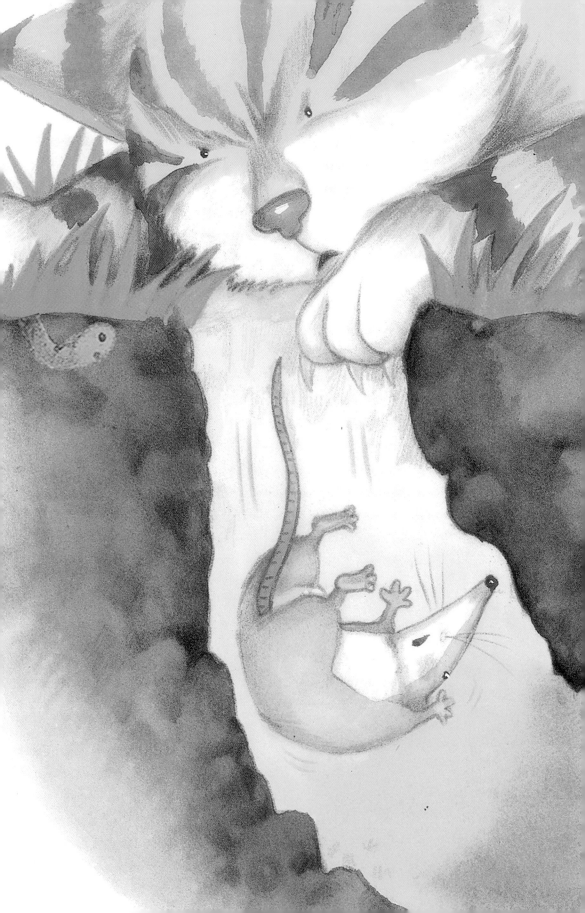

When Suki stops rolling and comes to rest, she finds herself staring straight at Bradley Rabbit. He holds a paw to his lips and beckons for Suki to follow him.

Bradley burrows a long tunnel away from where Ginger is lurking. He digs his way up to the surface, so that Suki can climb out. She darts back towards the counting post before Ginger sees her. 'Home safe!' she squeaks in excitement.
What a fun game!

Did you see these things?

Worm

Butterfly

Falling leaves

Beetle

Bluebird

On the Move

The elephant family are very busy indeed. They are moving to a new house, so they must pack all of their belongings into boxes. A van has arrived to carry everything away from their old home.

Mrs Elephant is making sure that fragile items are packed carefully so they don't get broken. Mr Elephant moves all of the heavy furniture. It isn't difficult as he is so strong!

Their son, Max, wants to help. He has made a big pile of things upstairs. All of his toys are in bags and boxes and cases, ready to carry down.

Mrs Elephant calls up to Max. 'Please will you pack your trunk now, and come downstairs?' she trumpets. Max looks at his trunk in the mirror and wonders what on earth she means.

Max chooses a suitcase that looks big enough to fit his trunk inside. He struggles for ages trying to fasten it. It really hurts!

When Max appears downstairs his parents burst out laughing. 'Oh, you poor silly elephant!' says his mum. She rubs Max's trunk gently to make it better, and gives him a kiss. 'I didn't mean you should pack your trunk in a case. A trunk is a special kind of suitcase used for storing things!'

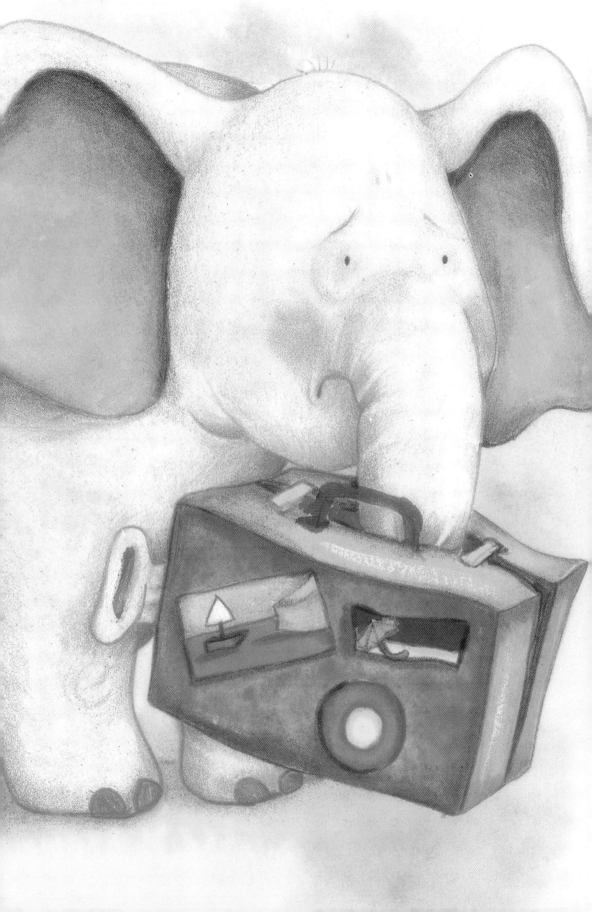

Read these words again

mirror	difficult
boxes	broken
suitcase	heavy
gently	fasten
laughing	belongings
fragile	struggles
furniture	downstairs

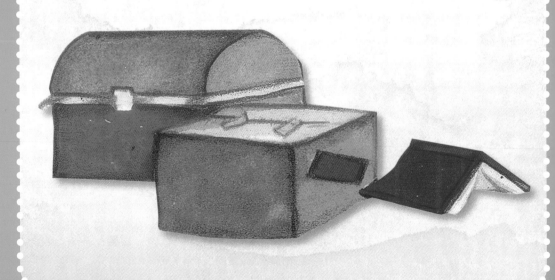

Did you see these things?

Green bag

Book

Lamp

Cardboard box

Hat

Travel sticker